J. S. BACH

Partitas Nos. IV-VI

BWV 828, 829 & 830

Edited by

WALTER EMERY

Fingered by

MAX PIRANI

THE ASSOCIATED BOARD OF
THE ROYAL SCHOOLS OF MUSIC

THE CONTEMPORARY EDITIONS

Bach's Mühlhausen cantatas of 1708 and 1709 (the latter lost) had been printed at the expense of the Town Council; with the Partitas he began to publish on his own account. The first was advertised on 1 November 1726; in translation, its title-page reads thus:

> Clavier Ubung [Keyboard Exercise]/ consisting of/ Preludes, Allemandes, Courantes, Sarabandes, Gigues, / Menuets, and other Galanteries;/ composed to refresh the spirits of music-lovers/ by /Johann Sebastian Bach,/ Acting Capellmeister to His Highness the Prince of Anhalt-Cöthen and/ Director of Choral Music at Leipzig./ Partita I./ Published by the Author/ 1726./

Bach took his terminology from his predecessor Kuhnau, who had published *Keyboard Exercises* in 1688 and 1692. Kuhnau's first volume contained seven Suites, called Partitas; his second volume, seven Partitas and a Sonata.

An autograph of Bach's Partita I, with a dedicatory poem, was prepared for the Prince of Cöthen's short-lived son; the poem was printed in 1879, before the whole MS unfortunately disappeared. This MS may have been presented to the Princess on 30 November 1726, her birthday; Bach seems to have gone to Cöthen to celebrate the occasion with Cantata 36a.

Partitas II and III were advertised on 19 September 1727; they could be had not only from Bach, but also from Böhm of Lüneburg and musicians in Dresden, Halle, Wolfenbüttel, Nuremberg, and Augsburg. The title-page of Partita IV is dated 1728. An advertisement of 1 May 1730 stated that Partita V was 'ready', and that 'the two still remaining' would be available at the Michaelmas Fair. It follows that Bach had intended to imitate Kuhnau in yet another way, and publish a set of *seven* Partitas; but for some reason he changed his mind, for there is no evidence that a seventh was ever even sketched. As for Partita VI, it was published singly like its predecessors; presumably at Michaelmas 1730, as promised. No copy of the single edition is known today; but the other five are so scarce that the total disappearance of the sixth is not surprising, and it certainly existed. In his *Lexicon* (1732), Walther remarked 'presumably it concludes the Opus'.

Having 'concluded the Opus', Bach published the six Partitas in a collected edition. The music plates of the single editions seem to have been etched by amateurs, and roughly handled; various dots and scratches were now more or less successfully cleared away, and the pages of Partitas II-VI were renumbered. In Partita VI, p.4 of the lost single edition became p.61 of the collected edition. There was no attempt at systematic correction, but a few ornaments were added by an etcher whose coarse work can be recognized in Partita VI as well as in some of the others. The title-page was done again in a more professional style, but its wording was largely identical with that quoted above. The *e* of *Clavier* was omitted: as the Prince of Cöthen had died in November 1728, Bach described himself as 'Acting Capellmeister to Weissenfels' (he had not bothered to do this in 1730, for Partita V): and the lines after 'Leipzig' were altered thus:

> OPUS I./ Published by the Author/ 1731./ Leipzig, on commission from the daughter and successor of the late Boetius, under the Rathaus./

The year of publication is thus known, but the month is not.

Five such copies still exist, perhaps six. On p.40, the page-number is on the wrong side of the page, and there is a mistake in the music (Partita IV, Courante, bar 5, q.v.). There are many other mistakes; these are here singled out merely because they are conspicuous.

Next, the last line of the title-page was deleted (with some damage to the date), and a few mistakes, including those on p.40, were corrected. About twenty copies have the altered title; all but one of them have the corrections on p.40. (I do not pretend to give exact figures. Private owners have tended to be secretive about their possessions; the result is that some copies seem to have disappeared, and others to have appeared from nowhere.) The title may have been corrected before p.40; but it seems more likely that Bach had both pages corrected at the same time. The title is not conjugate with the music pages: that is, it is on a separate sheet. Thus, a corrected title might easily have been sold with an uncorrected set of music pages.

Hitherto it has been supposed that Bach began by selling the collected edition himself, but tired of it, and handed over a small remainder to the Daughter of Boëtius, a bookseller; but the corrections on p.40 prove that the Boëtius copies are the earliest. Further, it is known that a Boëtius copy came into the possession of one F. H. Graff in 1731. He was a friend of Bach's, and is more likely to have had a first issue than a remainder.

The truth must therefore be that Bach began by selling through the Daughter of Boëtius, but soon cancelled the arrangement. His reason for doing so is not known. He cannot have had any serious quarrel with the lady, for in 1735 he was negotiating with her husband on behalf of his friend J. G. Walther.

In all copies of the collected edition, the music pages are numbered in arabic numerals. In two of the later (non-Boëtius) copies, there is an *additional* system of numbering by letters. This seems pointless; fortunately, as the music is unaffected, it is of no importance.

The various states of the collected edition (Boëtius title with mistakes on p.40: altered title: altered title with corrected p.40: numbering by letters) were first distinguished by Mr Richard Jones.

All the editions were etched on copper plates, and printed direct from the plates, like pictorial etchings today. Three men can be distinguished by their work. Etcher 1, who produced the single editions of Partitas I and II, was fairly competent. Etcher 2, who produced all the rest, made an amateurish job of Partita III, but improved thereafter. Etcher 3 made most of the corrections in the collected edition. His large thick shake-signs are very different from the thin wiry signs of his predecessors, and he tended to place them too late. These characteristics of his, revealed by comparing the single editions of Partitas III-V with the collected edition, can also be traced in Partita VI; but not in Partitas I and II – which, indeed, were hardly corrected at all. It is possible that Etcher 3 added the ∿ to Partita I, Corrente, bar 59; but if so, he must have left it unfinished, for it resembles his normal signs as little as it does those of the other etchers. As for the correction in Partita II, Courante, bar 19, it is a deletion; and naturally the etcher cannot be identified.

Besides the printed texts, there are a number of MSS. Most of them were copied from one or another of the editions; but the following have independent authority.

Partitas III and VI, in autograph, are the first two items in Anna Magdalena's Notebook of 1725. As compared with the printed versions, no.III lacks the Scherzo, no.VI the Air: the first movements are respectively two bars and three bars shorter: and there are other differences. None of the movements looks like a first draft, and two of them certainly are not.

Sonata VI for Violin and Clavier (BWV 1019) exists in three versions, of which the second has six movements. The third movement is a cembalo solo; the fifth was a violin solo accompanied by unfigured bass. The cembalo solo is in essentials the Corrente of Partita VI; its autograph is in the Berlin MS St.162. Of the fifth movement only the bass exists, again autograph, and in the same MS; very roughly, it agrees with the left-hand part of the Tempo di Gavotta of Partita VI, but is in G minor instead of E minor. The violin part, which has disappeared, was presumably more or less a transposition of the right-hand part of the Gavotta. These 'violin sonata' versions are clearly earlier than those in Anna Magdalena's Notebook.

ACKNOWLEDGEMENT

I owe much to Mr Richard Jones, who is preparing the NBA (Neue Bach Ausgabe) edition, for lending me microfilms and for spending a good deal of time in discussions that were profitable – possibly to him, certainly to me. His text will not agree with mine in every detail; but the music of Bach, like that of other 18th-century composers, has come down to us in such a confused state that opinions may legitimately differ.

WALTER EMERY
Salisbury, 1971-4

The Partitas must therefore have developed somewhat as follows:

1) Bach made and revised sketches as usual. No trace of these activities remains, except in the MSS of Partitas III and VI. Those of Partita VI remind us that these works may not have been conceived as wholes; they may have been patched together from movements originally written for violin sonatas or other purposes.

2) Bach made a revised fair copy of each Partita for the printer. All these copies have disappeared; they are represented by the single editions of Partitas I-V.

3) Bach revised the single editions for the collected edition; the results appear in the Boëtius copies.

4) At or about the time when the Boëtius line was deleted from the title-page, one correction was made in the music (Partita IV, Courante, bar 5).

It follows that, although the MSS and single editions are of great interest, they are so only because they throw light on mistakes and ambiguities in the non-Boëtius copies of the collected edition.

These mistakes and ambiguities are in fact quite common; and four of the surviving copies of the collected edition were partly corrected by hand. The most complete set of corrections is in the copy that formerly belonged to Paul Hirsch, and is now in the British Library (Hirsch III. 37). Many of the corrections are of no musical significance (rests are supplied in places where they were only technically necessary: accidentals are enlarged, as if to aid a weak-sighted man); but a fair number are of interest, and a few called for more critical ability than any editor has yet exhibited, so that one has to consider the possibility that they were authorized, if not actually made, by Bach himself. From these isolated rests, ornaments, accidentals, etc., one cannot prove that the writing is Bach's; but much of it might be. Moreover, the corrections resemble those that Bach made in a copy of the Clavierübung, Part II; and at the very least it is certain that the corrector had a thorough grasp of Bach's style. Whatever their origin, therefore, the Hirsch corrections are something to be thankful for; and the Hirsch copy has to be accepted as the primary source, although even it is by no means perfect.

THE PRESENT TEXT

The following abbreviations are used:

1726, etc.: the single edition of that year.

CE: the collected edition (1731), or its printed readings. All copies of CE have the same *printed* readings, except at one point, where the discrepancy is noted.

H: the Hirsch (non-Boëtius) copy of CE, or its MS corrections.

A: the autographs of Partitas III and VI in Anna Magdalena's Nótebook of 1725, or their readings.

V: the autograph fragments of Partita VI in the second version of Sonata VI for Violin and Clavier (BWV 1019).

Pitch-signs:

GG C c b c' c" c'''

For reasons given above H is the primary source. Its obvious mistakes are usually corrected without notice. This will suggest that H (CE) is more accurate than in fact it is – a point that must be borne in mind when considering doubtful passages – but at least it saves lists of dots that may either be missing or indistinguishable from flaws in the plates.

MS corrections in H are here all printed in normal type; but as they may disconcert readers who are used to other editions, all those that are musically significant are listed.

Deviations from H are of two kinds. Some are suggested by A; as far as possible, these are distinguished by *round* brackets. Others are editorial; as far as possible, these are distinguished in the usual ways, such as small type, *square* brackets, and ⌢. Deviations that cannot be dealt with thus easily are listed.

A small accidental above or below an ornament sign is an editorial suggestion referring to the auxiliary note of the ornament, not to the main note.

Appoggiaturas are not always slurred in CE; H adds a few slurs, but not consistently. Missing slurs have been supplied without notice.

Consistency is a state of the blessed to which few composers attain; but there is evidence that Bach occasionally aspired to it. In the autograph score of the B minor Mass, bars 61 and 115 of the first chorus are proof enough of that. In the Gigue of Partita VI, the bass of bar 17 (5th crotchet) is inconsistent with bar 35 (1st crotchet) in A; Bach corrected this in CE. I presume that he would have corrected other inconsistencies, if only he had noticed them. Such corrections are fully described, so that those who prefer the original text can easily revert to it.

·Finally, in Bach's day an accidental did not normally last throughout the bar. It applied only to the one note that it preceded, unless that note were immediately repeated; and if the note *were* repeated, the accidental lasted until the repetition stopped, even into the next bar. These rules were often broken; but it is most necessary to hear them in mind when using the List of Readings.

LIST OF READINGS

PARTITA IV

bar	*Ouverture*
9 rh	Ornament ∿, CE; this is improbable.
28 rh	Perhaps the second *d'* and the *e'* ought both to be sharp; cf. 107.
54-5 rh	Tie to *g"* very faint, CE.
74 lh	H adds ♯ to *g*, second beat.
95 lh	H adds tie to 96.
112	Final chord semibreve, CE (as here printed).

Allemande

4 rh — In 1728 and CE, the slur between the first two notes is represented by a wavy line (like ∿), sloping downwards to the right. In H this sign is heavily inked over, to make a slur.

6 lh — H adds stem to first note (*g*).

7 rh — H adds 3 below first group of triplets.

16-17 rh — As various misreadings are current, the passage is here transcribed:

The slur is very small, but it is there; and its position shows that it is a slur, not a tie across the barline.

23 rh — The tie from *d'* to 24 is duplicated by a meaningless tie to the *a* of 24; the etcher made a mistake, saw it, inserted the correct reading, but did not delete the mistake. Cf. 28 rh.

23 lh — First tenor note (*d*) should presumably be a quaver.

28 rh — See 4. 1728 has a similar wavy line, but shorter, and sloping slightly upwards. In CE a slur was added, but the wavy line was not deleted; cf. 23 rh. Some editors have read the wavy line (*between* the first two notes) as ∿ on *e"*: a piece of excessive ornamentation. H deletes the wavy line.

28 lh — H adds the first two rests.

32-4 rh — A transposed recapitulation of 13-15, with conspicuous variations on the last beats of 32-3. Those who regard the variations as deliberate should follow the main text (CE); but it is more probable that the variations were forced upon Bach by limitations of compass. The Gigue of Partita III (bar 21, in MS A) shows that in 1725 Bach was writing for a *c'''* keyboard: *c'''* is the highest note used in Partita IV: and note that in 34 of this Allemande, where there was no problem of compass, he printed an exact transposition of 15. The ossias to 32-3 provide exact transpositions of 13-14.

39 rh — CE has the meaningless slurring

40 rh — Non-Boëtius copies have the dot to the first note (*b'*); it is misplaced, above the lh ♯*a*.

44 rh — H adds slur.

47 lh — Fourth beat, ♯*G* placed too early; H adds a guide-line.

Courante

1 rh — ∿ to *d'*, H.

4 rh — Of the first appoggiatura (*d"*), only the head was etched; H adds stem and hook (not slur).

LIST OF READINGS

PARTITA IV (cont.)

5 lh Tenor ♩ ♩ ♫ in Boëtius copies of CE, ♩ ♫ ♩ in the later copies; the page-number (40) on the left-hand side in Boëtius copies, on the right in the later copies. In CE, the page-numbering is abnormal: right-hand pages have even numbers.

6 rh Second *b'* printed as ♯*c"* in CE; but cf. 1, 7, 8, etc.

14 rh Appoggiatura *g"*, CE.

20-22 rh Ornaments ∿ , CE; mistaken additions by Etcher 3. Bars 20 and 22 corrected, H.

36-7 rh Appoggiaturas added, H.

38 rh Appoggiatura editorial; cf. 14.

40 Etched thus, and uncorrected in H:

The bass is weak, and it can safely be called abnormal, for Bach's Courante cadences are usually of two well-defined types; see the E minor English Suite, etc., and for a closer parallel, BWV 818. Of the two types, Bach used one at 16; the other would be appropriate here, and has been adopted.

Aria

24 rh ♮♮♮♩♫ CE; H deletes the lower ∿ .

Sarabande

1 rh Some editors, encouraged by an early MS and by bar 13 as printed in CE, have tied the third and fourth notes (*d"*) as well as slurring the fourth and fifth notes. 1728 and CE have the slur, but not the tie.

6 rh Last note originally *a"*; ♯*f"* was added in 1728, and the *a"* never properly deleted. Cf. 5, 31.

13 rh Cf. 1, 29. Third and fourth notes tied, 1728: slur added, CE: tie deleted, H.

15 rh Ornament added above *b'*, CE. H did not delete it, but lengthened it towards the left, above ♯*c"*; he also added the slur.

17 rh No accidental to seventh note, CE. Literally, the note is ♮; but it is very likely that a ♯ was omitted as unnecessary, there being sharps before and after it.

28 rh H adds slur.

29 rh As in 1, 1728 and CE have the slur, but no tie; cf. 13.

31 rh Last note *g"*, CE; cf. 5, 6.

Menuet

6 rh ∿ , H.

8 rh Appoggiatura, H.

19 rh H adds the Turn, and *possibly* a staccato dot to the previous note.

25 rh ∿ , H.

28 lh H adds downstem and hook to fourth tenor note.

Gigue

27 rh Rest, H.

32 rh Here, as elsewhere in this movement, ♩⌢♪ is represented by ♩⌢.

64 rh H adds dot to ♯*a'*.

70 lh H adds dot to *e*, but not to rest.

PARTITA V

bar *Praeambulum*

84 rh Last note ♯*f'*, CE; cf. 30.

Allemande

1 rh Last note, ∿ added in CE (perhaps not by Etcher 3); transferred to previous note, H.

6 rh Slur to first two notes in one modern edition; not in CE.

10 rh Last two notes even semiquavers, CE; but cf. 26.

12 rh Last chord single-dotted, CE.

15 lh Appoggiatura and slur, H.

22 rh First and third ornaments added, H; second added CE.

26 rh CE omits dot to penultimate note.

28 rh Last chord single-dotted, CE.

Corrente

20 rh Precautionary ♮, H.

Sarabande

18 lh Only the head of the small note was etched; H failed to supply the stem and hooks, and partly obscured the head by enlarging the ♯. Bar 2 suggests that a semiquaver was intended.

20 rh Slur and small note added in CE.

22 rh 1730 has only the heads of the small notes; stems, hooks, and slurs added in CE. Upper slur before *g"* instead of after it.

38 lh ♩·♩ CE; ♩·𝄾♩ H.

Tempo di Minuetta

5 lh Third note *g"*, CE; cf. 45, etc.

Passepied

28 rh Appoggiatura (no slur), H.

29 rh ∿ across stem, CE; ∿ , H.

39 rh First note *g'*, CE; emended to *e'* in some editions, to agree with 37. Cf. 21, 23. Errors of a third are common; but *e'* seems harmonically improbable.

Gigue

13-14 rh Alto etched thus, CE:

Literally, the last note in 13 is natural; H adds a precautionary ♮. In 14, the extra space between the third and fourth notes suggests that an accidental was omitted.

17 lh Spacing of CE suggests that a ♯ to the second note was omitted; cf. 16.

53 rh Note that the first note of the second shake (♮*c"*) makes consecutive fifths.

61 rh Last alto note etched as ♪·, CE; hook erased, H.

LIST OF READINGS

PARTITA VI

bar   *Toccata*

Entitled *Prelude* in A.

5-6 rh   A has ∿ ; CE has the appoggiaturas. It is effective to play both.

9 lh   Slur (probably added by Etcher 3) too far to the right, CE; it seems to cover four quavers. Bars 11 and 23 show the correct reading.

21 lh   First slur as at 9, CE; second slur, H.

22 lh   Slurs, H.

23 rh   Second slur not in CE, because a new line begins with the fourth crotchet.

32 lh   Ought the last note to be ♯*G*, and the eighth note of 33 ♯ *A"*. Cf. 43-5.

43 rh   Ought the eighth note to be ♯*g*? Cf. 44 lh, last note.

45 lh   Editorial ♯ suggested by bar 43 rh, last note.

49-50 rh   Tie across bar-line from A.

73 lh   Third note *g*, CE; not ♮*f*, as in A and the parallel bars.

74-5   These bars are not in A.

74 lh   No ♮ to second *f*, CE.

75 lh   No ♮ to second *f*, CE (cf. 74).

90 lh   Tenor, ♯*f* minim, CE; so also A. In A, bar 2 originally had the parallel minim *b*; but Bach altered it to slurred crotchets *c' b*. He forgot to make the corresponding improvement in 90.

97 rh   At the ninth note, CE omits *e"*; cf. 94, 98 and especially 102.

104   Pauses, H.

105-7   These three bars in CE replace two bars (103-4) of A.

108 rh   Slur from *a'* to ♯*g'* (not ♯*d"* to *e"*), CE, A. No final pauses, CE.

Allemanda

2 rh   Small note, H; sloping stroke, A.

3 rh   Sloping strokes, A.

4   Arpeggio, A. In rh, Etcher 3 placed ∿ above the last note; corrected in H.

8   Notation of A:

CE has only the first upstem, and no dots; cf. 20.

13 rh   Third beat , CE. This has been transcribed in the usual way; but it must be admitted that the etcher ranged the *f"* with the lh *g'*, as if the three short notes were triplets.

15 rh   Small note, H.

16 lh   Second tie, H.

17 rh   Mordent, H.

20   Cf. 8; here CE has a dot to *e"*, as well as the upstem.

Corrente

36 lh   As the recapitulation is otherwise exact, the superior bass of 97-8 might be played here:

41 rh   Second note *a'*, V, A, CE; but see 102.

63 lh   Second note ♮ in V and A; most curiously, CE has ♭, in the old-fashioned way. H has ♮.

78 lh   First beat, CE has *B* as well as *b*; left uncorrected in H; *b* only, V and A.

79 rh   Bars 80-1 are a repetition of 2-3; perhaps 79 should be, as nearly as possible, a repetition of 1.

In V this was so:

But in A Bach altered bar 1, and retained this alteration in CE. He may have forgotten to make

79 agree, somewhat thus:

102 rh   In V, second note *d"*, parallel with *a'* in 41. A and CE have *e"* in 102, more closely parallel with the figuration of 43-5 and 104. Presumably *e"* is correct here, and *b'* in 41.

113   In V, A and CE, the lh plays the last *four* notes.

115-6 lh   V doubles the bass an octave higher.

Air

This movement is not in A.

8-10 rh   Slurs, H.

30   First rh note *e"*, second lh note *e'*, CE. Compare the sequence with those beginning in the second halves of 8 and 24; in 10 the corresponding figuration contains *d*, in 26, *d'*.

32   No final pauses, CE.

Sarabande

1 rh   The tie to *a'*, absent from some modern editions, is in CE.

5 rh   Bar 17 shows that the slur is correct as printed here; but in CE it connects ♯*d"* with *e"*. This may be a corruption – in some indirect way, a misreading of the misshapen mordent in A.

7 rh   Slur thus, CE. It may be misplaced, for it would make better sense if applied to the treble notes; cf. 5, 17.

7 lh   Second chord, *d'* from A; precautionary ♮ from A, H.

11 lh   H adds dot to fifth tenor note.

12   Arpeggio and sloping stroke from A.

15 lh   First note (♯*g*) preceded by what appears to be a clumsy attempt at a tie, CE; proper tie added later.

16 lh   H has a mistaken correction, a dot to the minim *e*. It is in paler ink than the genuine corrections, and may not have been made by the same man.

17   Arpeggio from A.

18 rh   Sloping strokes from A.

19 rh   Slur from A.

22 rh   Small notes etched without stems, CE; H supplies only the second stem.

23 rh   Despite the consecutives, the slide sign begins on *b'* in A and CE. Cf. 35.

24   Arpeggios from A. On third beat, lower three notes of rh chord etched as crotchets, as in A; quaver hooks and dots, H. H also adds dots to lh *c* and *e*.

25 lh   Ornaments from A.

PARTITA VI (cont.)

28 rh	H adds demisemiquaver bar to *second* ♯*f"*.
30 lh	The *e'* in the last chord was etched twice, first on leger lines above the bass stave and then on the treble stave, and so left. Despite the leger lines, some people have read the former *e'* as *b* or *c'*; H deletes it.
34 lh	Third beat from A. CE has *B* crotchet – that is, omits the quaver hook and rest.
35 rh	Appoggiatura makes consecutive fifths; cf. 23. Once again, the ornament is in A as well as CE, and is perfectly clear.
36 lh	Beneath the stave, in the *F* space and *after* the *E* minim, CE has a wavy line that can be read as a shake sign with three humps. Placed as it is, the sign is meaningless; but it is just conceivable that Bach wrote ∿ to the rh *e'*, and that Etcher 2 placed it below the bass stave instead of above the treble. It must nevertheless be admitted that the wavy line may be nothing more than an accidental scratch in the plate.

Gigue
In A, the time-signature is ₵, and the notes are half the length of those in CE. In A, Bach sometimes wrote ♪♪♪♪ where CE has ♪♪♪♪ or ♪♪♪♪; there seems no solid reason to believe that CE is wrong.

8 rh	Tie to *b'* too far to the right, CE; probably added by Etcher 3.
19 lh	Tenor, third and fourth notes should perhaps be ♩. ♪ as in A; cf. 44 rh.
20 rh	CE omits dots to *a'* (third crotchet) and *e'* (fifth crotchet).
24 rh	Ties and small notes editorial; see 52.
26 lh	Shakes in the subject etched as ∿, here and later; H adds the hook everywhere and the vertical stroke everywhere but here. These shakes thus became partial inversions of those in the first half of the piece. Note that the shake in 50 is editorial; and that, if played, it must not be of the inverted type.
30 lh	∿ from A, where it is confused with a stave-line and easily overlooked.
48 rh	CE omits tie to *b*, small *b*, and downstem to *f'*; cf. 47.
51 rh	Last crotchet, etcher omitted *f'* and tie, and placed the ♮ too far to the right. Corrected in H.
52 rh	Ties and small notes partly editorial. In A, downstems to *e'* and ♯*g'* (not to *b'*) imply that the whole chord is to be sustained.

Bach used arpeggio signs only occasionally, as in the Allemande of Partita V and the Sarabande of Partita VI; but it is well known that, on the harpsichord, any chord that is at all thick sounds better spread. Opinions may differ on whether a chord is thick or not, and much depends on such individual matters as tempo, about which it is absurd to lay down rules; but the possibility should be borne in mind.

The interpretations given in ossias are editorial suggestions for shakes, etc. Each is meant to apply to other ornaments of the *same* kind, in the *same* movement.

Many of the shake signs in CE are ambiguous. No one can tell whether they are short or long; no editor, therefore, can do more than print what he thinks most suitable. Even when a sign is clear, it may be wrong.

In my interpretations I have sometimes begun plain shakes (∿ ∿) with the main note. Those who believe that *all* such shakes begin with the upper note can easily adjust matters to suit themselves.

Some of my orthodox interpretations imply tempi that may seem unduly slow. Bach's tempi may have been slower than those acceptable today; no one knows, and in any case, authenticity can be carried too far. The right tempo for today is not necessarily Bach's; it is one that will keep a present-day audience awake. Players who find my ossias too elaborate should not hesitate for a moment to simplify them, so long as they retain the general outline of the ornament.

PARTITA IV

Ouverture, bars 36 and 40. The first appoggiatura is a quaver, the second a semiquaver; but presumably they have the same meaning.

Allemande, bars 13 and 32, rh. Note that the *written-out* appoggiaturas, on the first beat, are inconsistent. It seems hardly necessary to rectify them.

Bars 14-15, 33-4, rh. Some may feel that the third quavers of these bars need some such ornamentation as this (bar 14):

Courante, bar 6, rh. The interpretation was suggested by the *written-out* appoggiatura in bar 8. It might also be applied to bar 32, but seems less effective there.

Aria, bars 4-7, lh. The long *A* will probably need to be re-struck.

Bar 24, rh. See List of Readings. The slur and *both* ornaments were added by Etcher 3. As he often placed signs too far to the right, it is possible that the shake ought to be on *e"*, and that he did not trouble to delete his erroneous shake to ♯*d"* (cf. Partita VI, Sarabande, bar 30 lh); but when two notes are slurred like this, the shake is usually on the second note, and H corrects the passage accordingly. Bar 40 seems to be an exception to this 'rule'. When considering these passages, note that the half-cadences in bars 4 and 8 are not slurred.

ORNAMENTS

PARTITA V

Allemande. The slurs to the shakes in bars 2, 10 and 26 can be treated as ties; but this cannot be done in bar 6, where there is no slur, and the rhythm will be broken unless ♯*c″* is struck *on* the second quaver. On the whole, it seems likely that the above-mentioned slurs are *not* ties, and that bar 14 should be treated similarly.

Bar 22. The second ornament is not in 1730, but was added to CE by Etcher 3; it is thus quite likely to be in some way wrong. Those who feel that there are too many ornaments in this bar will probably do well to omit the second.

Corrente, bar 23, rh. The two staccato dots and the shake, all in 1730, are untouched in CE and H; and the shake is clearly a long one with closing-notes. Such a shake cannot be played staccato. Perhaps the best solution is to shorten the shake:

Sarabande. The appoggiaturas are very small; but a microscope shows that the two in the initial upbeat, and the lh one in bar 2, were etched as semiquavers. Of that in bar 18, lh, only the head was etched; but cf. bar 2. All the rest are quavers. Those in bars 4, 20 and 22 have nevertheless been interpreted as crotchets, by analogy with the *written-out* double appoggiatura in bar 34.

In bar 2, however, the notation seems best taken literally – on the first beat, that is. It seems to matter little whether the *second* rh appoggiatura is a quaver or a semiquaver, and the same goes for bars 10, 11 and 35.

The ornamentation from the beginning of the piece to the middle of bar 2 should be applied to the parallel phrases beginning in bars 4, 16 and 32; but is less desirable, if not actually impossible, in bars 21-3 and 34-5.

PARTITA VI

Toccata, bar 104. On the harpsichord, if not on the piano, the chord on the third beat can be spread somewhat thus (the accents show the positions of the beats):

Sarabande. All chords that are at all thick should be spread, whether so marked or not. Sloping strokes can be treated as in the initial ossia. Some of them are in A, but not in CE (see the List of Readings); there seems no reason to suppose that Bach omitted them deliberately, and they are very effective.

Listeners will find this piece easier to follow if *something* is struck on almost every crotchet beat. The slurred shake in bar 4 is therefore best begun with the main note, as shown: so too the parallel bar 16: so too the *first* shake in bar 28 (although here it is the *quaver* beat that needs to be

exhibited): and bar 31 lh. In bar 32, other notes are struck on the second beat, and the lh shake can be tied; but this shake ought perhaps to be parallel with that in bar 31. In bar 23 lh, the slur can be taken as a tie, so that the shake runs in tenths with the rh.

The closing-notes of the shakes in bars 8, 27 and 30 can, of course, be played at the same speed as the previous notes of the shakes.

As for the appoggiaturas, the ossias are merely bases for experiment. The best interpretations will depend on tempo, on double-dotting, and on whether the player adds ornaments of his own. The ossia to bar 1 gives an orthodox interpretation; but it is conceivable (by analogy with bars 5-8, 13, 17, 19) that the discordant *b* ought to resolve on the second crotchet, rather than on the second quaver.

At bar 35 the appoggiatura makes fifths (cf. bar 23); and here the problem is complicated by the nakedness of the *g′* (followed by closing-notes), which seems to call for a shake. The small note can be regarded as a *Nachschlag*, and played before the beat; the result (adding a shake) is then contrapuntally blameless but the context is a strange one, both for a *Nachschlag* and for a main-note shake. Perhaps it is better to face the fifths!

The mordent in bar 5 raises a curious point. It is not in CE (unless the slur from ♯*d″* to *e″* is a corruption of it; see the List of Readings), but it is in A; and it is printed here because bar 5 is roughly parallel with bar 17, and in bar 17 both A and CE have a corresponding mordent.

In bar 7, A has another corresponding mordent, on *d″*. In CE this is replaced perhaps because it is awkward to play, by the four slurred demisemiquavers (which amount to a Turn). In the parallel bar 19, A has a mordent on *g′*; replaced in CE, perhaps for the same reason, by the two *left-hand* demisemiquavers (which amount to a mordent on *e′*, played before the beat).

The second beat of the bar 6 has no ornament in A; but in CE the lh has a 'Turn', corresponding to that in bar 7 rh.

Such are the facts. As the rh mordent in bar 17 is just as awkward as those in bars 7 and 19 of A, did Bach mean the figuration of bar 17 to agree with that of bar 19 in CE? And what of bar 5?

DOUBLE-DOTTING

PARTITA IV

Ouverture. In CE, the final rh quavers of bars 5, 6 and 11 are ranged as here, with the final lh semiquavers. The ranging of CE is erratic, and this sort of thing does not amount to proof; but it does at least suggest that the figure ♩. ♪ should be double-dotted. The last quaver of bar 12 should be treated in the same way, and perhaps the fourth quaver of bar 5, although it is ranged as a quaver. It is legitimate to go further, and treat ♪♪♩ as ♪♪..♩ wherever it occurs.

PARTITA V

Sarabande. In bars 9, 10 (probably), 11, 13, 23 and 35, the isolated rh quavers are ranged with lh semiquavers; this, as explained above, is at least suggestive. In bar 38 lh, the etched ♪· ♪ is corrected to ♪· 𝄾♪ in H. Compare bar 18 lh with bar 2 (third beat); and the phrases beginning with quavers in bars 4, 20 and 22, with the first note of the piece and its parallels (all semiquavers) in bars 16, 32 and 34. Clearly, ♪· ♪ needs to be double-dotted wherever it occurs.

PARTITA VI.

Toccata. It is tempting to double-dot the figure ♪·♪ in the first and third sections of this piece. Note, however, that as the material of bars 9-10 (etc.) recurs at bars 72 and 76, all three sections go at more or less the same tempo; and as that tempo will be fairly brisk, the first beat of bar 26 is best left alone. Moreover, at this point the rh has ♪♬♬ (no mordent) in A. In CE, Bach sharpened the rhythm; it may be wrong to go further than he did.

Allemanda. In bars 2-4, and again at the *third* beat of bar 19 lh, ♪♪♩ is ranged as if it were ♪♪..♩ (cf. Partitas IV and V, above). It is not so ranged elsewhere, and my suggestions in bars 13, 14 and 17 need not be taken seriously. The even semiquavers in bars 2, 4, 13 and 14 look wrong; but if Bach had wanted ♪♪..♩, he could have written it here just as well as he did in almost every other bar of this piece.

Sarabande. Double-dotting is at first sight desirable; but there is little in its favour. In bar 33 the rh figure ♪♪♩ is three times ranged as if it were ♪♪..♩ ; but that is merely suggestive, and the lh parts of bars 8-9 and 20-21 are not so treated. In bar 30 rh it may be that the second and third beats ought to have the same rhythmic pattern (that the treble of the third beat ought to be ♪♪..♩), and that the lh ought to follow suit. But that is all, apart from personal taste. One may reasonably experiment with double-dotting the initial up-beat and the chordal passage that starts in bar 2, with their parallels; leaving the rest alone, except perhaps for the above-mentioned bars 30 and 33.

TRIPLETS

PARTITA IV

Allemande. As a matter of interest, note that whereas bar 10 has triplets at the fifth quaver, the parallel bar 45 has ♬♬ .

Menuet. The even quavers in bars 10, 12 and 28 might be played as triplets, and something might even be done with bars 21-2; but it seems unnecessary.

PARTITA V

Allemande. In bar 1, etc., the figure ♪ ♪♪ might mean $\frac{24}{16}$ ♪ ♪♪ ; but the interpretation here recommended runs in tenths with the rh at the sixth quaver. The slurred even semiquavers in bars 4, 5 and 24 seem to flow most naturally as $\frac{24}{16}$ ♪♪ , though admittedly it is hard to see why Bach did not write ♪♪ , as he did elsewhere. In bars 17-19 the figure ♪♪♪ might be read as $\frac{24}{16}$ ♪♪ ♪♪ ; but this is hardly credible in the alto of bar 20. In bar 25 there may well be better ways of adapting the printed figuration; but adapted it must be.

PARTITA VI

Tempo di Gavotta. The first thing one has to realize is that in the C minor Cello Suite (BWV 1011) Gavotte II begins

thus:

and is, as far as the listener can tell, entirely in $\frac{12}{8}$. There is therefore no historico-aesthetic reason why the present piece, called not *Gavotte* but *Tempo di Gavotta*, should not be in $\frac{12}{8}$.

Comparison of V, A and CE shows Bach replacing the figure ♬♬ by ♬♬♬ in bar 13 lh, beat 1: 13 rh, beat 3: 20 lh, beat 3; and using ♬♬♬ from the outset in bar 13 lh, beat 3 and 21 lh, beat 3. More striking still, at bar 12 V (transposed) has ♪♪♪♪♪♪ . This is a direct reference to the rhythm of the subject. In A the part lies differently, but ♬♬ is translated into triplets ♪♪♪♪♪♪ Finally, in CE (see the present text) the reference to the subject is thrown overboard.

As for the figure ♩ ♬♬♬ in bars 6, 14, 22 and 26, there may be better ways of adapting it; but as the piece is clearly meant to be played in $\frac{12}{8}$, adapted it must be (cf. Partita V, Allemande, bar 25).

PARTITA IV
BWV 828

JOHANN SEBASTIAN BACH
(1685-1750)

Ouverture*

* See Preface, under Double-dotting

Allemande *

* See Preface, under Ornaments and Triplets

A.B.1736

Courante

Aria*

* See Preface, under Ornaments

Sarabande

28

Menuet *

Gigue

* See Preface, under Triplets

A.B.1736

PARTITA V
BWV 829

Praeambulum

Allemande*

Corrente

Sarabande*

42

Tempo di Minuetta

A.B.1736

Passepied

PARTITA VI
BWV 830

Toccata *

* See Preface, under Ornaments and Double-dotting

A. B. 1736

Allemanda *

A. B. 1736

* See Preface, under Double-dotting

Corrente

Air

The notation is approximate;
the accents show the positions of the beats

Sarabande*

* See Preface, under Ornaments and Double-dotting

Tempo di Gavotta *

* See Preface, under Ornaments and Triplets

A.B.1736

Gigue

Finis

A.B.1736

Printed by Caligraving Limited Thetford Norfolk England